THE GET UP AND GO DIARY FOR BUSY WOMEN

ISBN 978-1-9

G

A busy, vibrant, goal-oriented woman is so much more attractive than a woman who waits around for a man to validate her existence.

Mandy Hale

GetUpandGo Publications
WE ASPIRE TO INSPIRE

Published in Ireland by

GET UP AND GO PUBLICATIONS LTD

Unit 7A Cornhill Business Complex, Ballyshannon, Co Donegal, F94 C4AA.

Email: info@getupandgodiary.com

www.getupandgodiary.com

Compiled by the Get Up and Go team
Graphic Design by Rosie Gray
Illustrations: freepik.com
Printed in Ireland by GPS Colour Graphics

2025 BANK AND PUBLIC HOLIDAYS

REPUBLIC OF IRELAND

New Year's Day, 1 January;
St Patrick's Day, 17 March;
Easter Monday, 21 April;
June Bank Holiday, 2 June;
October Bank Holiday, 27 October;
St Stephen's Day, 26 December.

St Brigid's Day, 3 February;
Good Friday, 18 April;
May Day Bank Holiday, 5 May;
August Bank Holiday, 4 August;
Christmas Day, 25 December;

NORTHERN IRELAND

New Year's Day, 1 January;
Good Friday, 18 April;
May Day Holiday, 5 May;
Orangemen's Holiday, 12 July;
Christmas Day, 25 December;

St Patrick's Day, 17 March;
Easter Monday, 21 April;
Spring Bank Holiday, 26 May;
Summer Bank Holiday, 25 August;
Boxing Day, 26 December.

ENGLAND, SCOTLAND AND WALES

New Year's Day, 1 January;
Easter Monday, 21 April;
May Day Holiday, 5 May;
Summer Bank Holiday, 25 August;
Christmas Day, 25 December;

Good Friday, 18 April;
St George's Day, 23 April;
Spring Bank Holiday, 26 May;
Remembrance Day, 11 November;
Boxing Day, 26 December.

UNITED STATES OF AMERICA

New Year's Day, 1 January;
Presidents' Day, 17 February;
Independence Day, 4 July;
Columbus Day, 13 October;
Thanksgiving Day, 27 November;

Martin Luther King Day, 20 January;
Memorial Day, 26 May;
Labour Day, 1 September;
Veterans Day, 11 November;
Christmas Day, 25 December.

CANADA

New Year's Day, 1 January;
Heritage Day, 17 February;
St Patrick's Day, 17 March;
Easter Monday, 21 April;
Canada Day, 1 July;
Thanksgiving Day, 13 October;
Christmas Day, 25 December;

Family Day, 17 February;
Commonwealth Day, 10 March;
Good Friday, 18 April;
Victoria Day 19 May;
Labour Day, 1 September;
Rememberance Day, 11 November;
Boxing Day, 26 December.

AUSTRALIA (NATIONAL HOLIDAYS)

New Year's Day, 1 January;
Good Friday, 18 April;
Anzac Day, 25 April;
Christmas Day, 25 December;

Australia Day, 27 January;
Easter Monday, 21 April;
King's Birthday, 10 June;
Boxing Day, 26 December.

2025 CALENDAR

January

Su	Mo	Tu	We	Th	Fr	Sa
29	30	31	1	2	3	4
5	6	7	8	9	10	11
12	13	14	15	16	17	18
19	20	21	22	23	24	25
26	27	28	29	30	31	1

February

Su	Mo	Tu	We	Th	Fr	Sa
26	27	28	29	30	31	1
2	3	4	5	6	7	8
9	10	11	12	13	14	15
16	17	18	19	20	21	22
23	24	25	26	27	28	1

March

Su	Mo	Tu	We	Th	Fr	Sa
23	24	25	26	27	28	1
2	3	4	5	6	7	8
9	10	11	12	13	14	15
16	17	18	19	20	21	22
23	24	25	26	27	28	29
30	31	1	2	3	4	5

April

Su	Mo	Tu	We	Th	Fr	Sa
30	31	1	2	3	4	5
6	7	8	9	10	11	12
13	14	15	16	17	18	19
20	21	22	23	24	25	26
27	28	29	30	1	2	3

May

Su	Mo	Tu	We	Th	Fr	Sa
27	28	29	30	1	2	3
4	5	6	7	8	9	10
11	12	13	14	15	16	17
18	19	20	21	22	23	24
25	26	27	28	29	30	31

June

Su	Mo	Tu	We	Th	Fr	Sa
1	2	3	4	5	6	7
8	9	10	11	12	13	14
15	16	17	18	19	20	21
22	23	24	25	26	27	28
29	30	1	2	3	4	5

July

Su	Mo	Tu	We	Th	Fr	Sa
29	30	1	2	3	4	5
6	7	8	9	10	11	12
13	14	15	16	17	18	19
20	21	22	23	24	25	26
27	28	29	30	31	1	2

August

Su	Mo	Tu	We	Th	Fr	Sa
27	28	29	30	31	1	2
3	4	5	6	7	8	9
10	11	12	13	14	15	16
17	18	19	20	21	22	23
24	25	26	27	28	29	30
31	1	2	3	4	5	6

September

Su	Mo	Tu	We	Th	Fr	Sa
31	1	2	3	4	5	6
7	8	9	10	11	12	13
14	15	16	17	18	19	20
21	22	23	24	25	26	27
28	29	30	1	2	3	4

October

Su	Mo	Tu	We	Th	Fr	Sa
28	29	30	1	2	3	4
5	6	7	8	9	10	11
12	13	14	15	16	17	18
19	20	21	22	23	24	25
26	27	28	29	30	31	1

November

Su	Mo	Tu	We	Th	Fr	Sa
26	27	28	29	30	31	1
2	3	4	5	6	7	8
9	10	11	12	13	14	15
16	17	18	19	20	21	22
23	24	25	26	27	28	29
30	1	2	3	4	5	6

December

Su	Mo	Tu	We	Th	Fr	Sa
30	1	2	3	4	5	6
7	8	9	10	11	12	13
14	15	16	17	18	19	20
21	22	23	24	25	26	27
28	29	30	31	1	2	3

FORGIVE THE PAST - LET IT GO
LIVE THE PRESENT - THE POWER OF NOW
CREATE THE FUTURE - THOUGHTS BECOME THINGS

Dear Reader,

Welcome to the 2025 edition of the Get Up and Go Diary for Busy Women. If this is your first Get Up and Go diary, you are about to embark on a wonderful journey with the world's best loved inspirational diary. If you are one of our many regular loyal customers, we trust you will enjoy this latest edition of your much-loved diary. Whether you have chosen this diary for yourself or received it as a gift, it will fill your days with inspiration, enlightenment, and encouragement.

You can use your Get Up and Go Diary as a diary or for journalling. Journalling is a powerful tool for personal growth and development. It allows you to reflect on/ remember past experiences, set goals, record progress, create your future, and can help keep you on track.

As a "thank you" to you, our customer, a contribution from each diary becomes a "Giving Impact" in support of worthy causes in the developing world, through our partnership with B1G1 – Business for Good (www.B1G1.com). The paper for our diaries is sourced from FSC certified suppliers. "FSC, the world's leading ethical wood label, says its branding tells shoppers the products come from legal and sustainable sources" (https://fsc.org). Get Up and Go Publications Ltd has been accredited as an All-Ireland Business Foundation All Star Best in Class Inspirational Publication for the sixth year in a row (www.AIBF.ie).

If you would like to purchase additional copies, view our full range of diaries and journals, or subscribe to our monthly newsletter please visit www.getupandgodiary.com. Subscribing to our newsletter will connect you with our growing Get Up and Go community, keeping you informed about our newest products and priority discounts. You may also like to follow us on Facebook: The Irish Get Up and Go Diary; Twitter: @getupandgo1; or Instagram: @Page 1 Instagram: Getupandgodiaries. If you love our Get Up and Go Diaries or Journals, please share our details with your family and friends.

Best wishes for 2025!

From the team at Get Up and Go Publications Ltd

This diary belongs to: _____

Address: _____

Tel: _____ Email: _____

Emergency Telephone Number: _____

HAPPY NEW YEAR

Bucket list for *January*

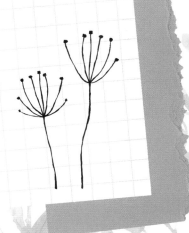

January

Another year, another start,
A time of hope for every heart,
A time to leave the past behind.
And share a newfound peace of mind.
Then going forward day by day,
Find love and joy along life's way.

Iris Hesswlden

Wednesday **01**	New Years Day
	Bank Holiday

The future is created, not promised to anyone

Thursday **02**

Happiness is a choice

Friday **03**

Keep your thoughts and feelings in harmony with your actions

Saturday **04**

Teach people how to treat you by treating them the same

Sunday **05**

Focus your energy on what you need to handle now

January

Nobody can go back and start a new beginning, but anyone can start today and make a new ending.

Mary Robinson

Monday **06**

Your life is in order, manage your moments.

Tuesday **07**

Appreciate your community

Wednesday **08**

Procrastination is not always bad ... timing is everything

Thursday **09**

Choose the healthy option

Friday **10**

There are many answers to a single question

Saturday **11**

Reignite your passion

Sunday **12**

Don't deny yourself the right to a great life

January

Love is a fire. But whether it is going to warm your heart or burn the house down, you can never tell.

Joan Crawford

Monday **13**

Wolf Moon

Prepare well to achieve well

Tuesday **14**

Keep it simple

Wednesday **15**

Be at peace with yourself and others

Thursday 16

Allocate time for family and friends

Friday 17

It is enough to be who you are

Saturday 18

Never speak little of yourself

Sunday 19

See the beauty in yourself

January

Women are never stronger than when they arm themselves with their weaknesses.

Madame Marie du Deffand

Monday 20

Stumbling is not falling

Tuesday 21

Create your home as the place you love to come home to

Wednesday 22

Believe in the power of one

Thursday **23**

Life is all about chance, choice and change

Friday **24**

Keep your ideals high and raise your standards

Saturday **25**

It's ok to have quiet days

Sunday **26**

Do the things you have always wanted to do

January

There came a time when the risk to remain tight in the bud was more painful than the risk it took to blossom.

Anais Nin

Monday **27**

Avoid worry; think and plan

Tuesday **28**

Choose to see the world through grateful eyes

Wednesday **29**   New Moon

We all have many lessons to learn

Thursday **30**

Choose your family as they are

Friday **31**

Take the time to get a medical check up

*I shall pass through this life but once.
Any good therefore that I can do,
let me do it now.
Let me not defer or neglect it.
For I shall never pass this way again.*

Etienne de Grellet

When looking for a life partner, my advice to women is date all of them: the bad boys, the cool boys, the commitment-phobic boys, the crazy boys. But do not marry them. The things that make the bad boys sexy do not make them good husbands. When it comes time to settle down, find someone who wants an equal partner. Someone who thinks women should be smart, opinionated and ambitious. Someone who values fairness and expects or, even better, wants to do his share in the home. These men exist and trust me, over time, nothing is sexier.

Sheryl Sandberg

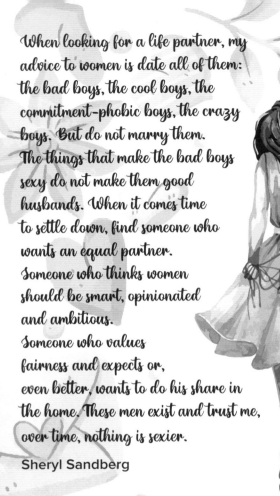

Do not bring people in your life who weigh you down. And trust your instincts ... good relationships feel good. They feel right. They don't hurt. They're not painful. That's not just with somebody you want to marry, but it's with the friends that you choose. It's with the people you surround yourselves with.

Michelle Obama

Bucket list for *February*

> You know it's love when all you want is that person to be happy, even if you're not part of their happiness.

Julia Roberts

February

HUGGING

Hugging is healthy. It keeps the immune system, cures depression, reduces stress and induces sleep. It's invigorating, rejuvenating and has no unpleasant side effects. Hugging is nothing less than a miracle drug.

Hugging is all natural. It is organic, naturally sweet, no artificial ingredients, non-polluting, environmentally friendly and a 100 percent wholesome.

Hugging is the ideal gift. It is great for any occasion, fun to give and receive, shows you care, comes with its own wrapping and, of course, is fully returnable.

Hugging is practically perfect. No batteries to wear out, inflation-proof, non-fattening, no monthly payments, theft-proof and non-taxable.

Hugging is an under-utilised resource with magical powers. When we open our hearts and arms, we encourage others to do the same.

Think of the people in your life. Are there any words you would like to say? Are there any hugs you want to share? Are you waiting and hoping someone else will ask first?

Please don't wait! Initiate!!

Charles Faraone

It takes courage to love, but pain through love is the purifying fire which those who love generously know. We all know people who are so much afraid of pain that they shut themselves up like clams in a shell and, giving out nothing, receive nothing and therefore shrink until life is a mere living death.

Eleanor Roosevelt

Saturday **01**

Schedule a 'date night'

Sunday **02**

Your life is your responsibility

February

Do not think that love, in order to be genuine, has to be extraordinary. What we need is to love without getting tired.

Mother Teresa

Monday **03**

St Brigid's Day
Bank Holiday

Stay aligned with your purpose in life

Tuesday **04**

Be true to yourself

Wednesday **05**

The world is truly an amazing place

Thursday **06**

All motivation is self-motivation

Friday **07**

Things don't matter, people do

Saturday **08**

Your best is always good enough

Sunday **09**

What you do makes a difference

February

What we have once enjoyed we can never lose.
All that we love deeply becomes a part of us.

Helen Keller

Monday **10**

We all have all the time there is

Tuesday **11**

Attitude is everything

Wednesday **12**   Snow Moon

Happy is the new rich

Thursday 13

Trust is the foundation of any worthwhile relationship

Valentine's Day

Friday 14

Have dinner by candlelight

Saturday 15

Let those who love you help you

Sunday 16

Do something today that you love doing

February

We are not held back by the love we didn't receive in the past, but by the love we're not extending in the present.

Marianne Williamson

Monday **17**

Life always gives us second chances

Tuesday **18**

Be a supportive friend

Wednesday **19**

Courage and confidence come from within

Thursday **20**

Put an extra squeeze in your hugs today

Friday **21**

Today's food choices create tomorrows health

Saturday **22**

Expect and accept the unexpected

Sunday **23**

Accept the gift of acknowledgement

February

Truly loving another means letting go of all expectations. It means full acceptance, even celebration of another's personhood.

Karen Casey

Monday **24**

The more you look the more you see

Tuesday **25**

Count your blessings

Wednesday **26**

Let go of what you can't control

Thursday 27

Don't react, take time to respond

Friday 28

Hold on to your dream, it's yours

A woman has got to love a bad man once or twice in her life, to be thankful for a good one.

Marjorie Kinnan

Nobody cares if you can't dance well. Just get up and dance. Great dancers are not great because of their technique, they are great because of their Passion.

Martha Graham

Goats Cheese Risotto with Pesto

INGREDIENTS:

- 2 tbsp olive oil, for frying
- 200g risotto rice
- 700ml chicken stock or vegetable stock
- 1 carton fresh pesto
- 100g soft goat's cheese

METHOD:

STEP 1
Pour the olive oil into a large saucepan. Add the rice and fry for 1 min. Add half the stock and cook until absorbed. Add the remaining stock, a little at a time, and cook until the rice is al dente, stirring continually, for 20-25 mins.

STEP 2
Stir through half the goat's cheese and the pesto. Serve topped with the remaining goat's cheese.

Bucket list for *March*

If we don't change, we don't grow.
If we don't grow, we are not really living.
Growth demands a temporary surrender of security.

Gail Sheehy

WHEN GOD CREATED MOTHERS   Erma Bombeck

When the Good Lord was creating mothers, He was into His sixth day of 'overtime' when the angel appeared and said. "You're doing a lot of fiddling around on this one."

And God said, "Have you read the specs on this order? She has to be completely washable, but not plastic. Have 180 moveable parts...all replaceable. Run on black coffee and leftovers. Have a lap that disappears when she stands up. A kiss that can cure anything from a broken leg to a disappointed love affair. And six pairs of hands." The angel shook her head slowly and said. "Six pairs of hands.... no way."

"It's not the hands that are causing me problems," God remarked, "it's the three pairs of eyes that mothers have to have."

"That's on the standard model?" asked the angel. God nodded.

One pair that sees through closed doors when she asks, "What are you kids doing in there?" when she already knows. Another here in the back of her head that sees what she shouldn't but what she has to know, and of course the ones here in front that can look at a child when he goofs up and say. "I understand and I love you" without so much as uttering a word.

"God," said the angel touching his sleeve gently, "Get some rest tomorrow....."

"I can't," said God, "I'm so close to creating something so close to myself. Already I have one who heals herself when she is sick...can feed a family of six on one pound of hamburger...and can get a nine year old to stand under a shower."

The angel circled the model of a mother very slowly. "It's too soft," she sighed.

"But tough!" said God excitedly. "You can imagine what this mother can do or endure."

"Can it think?"

"Not only can it think, but it can reason and compromise," said the Creator.

Finally, the angel bent over and ran her finger across the cheek.

"There's a leak," she pronounced. "I told You that You were trying to put too much into this model."

"It's not a leak," said the Lord, "It's a tear."

"What's it for?"

"It's for joy, sadness, disappointment, pain, loneliness, and pride."

"You are a genius," said the angel.

Somberly, God said, "I didn't put it there."

March

"My will shall shape the future.
Whether I fail or succeed shall be
no one's doing but my own.
I am the force. I can clear any
obstacle before me or I can be
lost in the maze. My choice.
My responsibility.
Win or lose; only I hold
the key to my destiny."

Elaine Maxwell

Saturday **01**

Happiness is an advantage

Sunday **02**

Focus on the task in hand

March

Blessed are those who can give without remembering and take without forgetting.

Elizabeth Bibesco

Monday **03**

Honour and value yourself

Tuesday **04**　　　　　　　Pancake day

Happiness boosts your immune system

Wednesday **05**

Remove should, could and would from your vocabulary

Thursday **06**

Keep going; you're nearly there

Friday **07**

Charm is an inexpensive quality

Saturday **08**

Be genuinely interested in others

Sunday **09**

Be careful not to misinterpret a situation

March

A girl should be two things: classy and fabulous.

Coco Chanel

Monday **10**

Break a habit of a lifetime

Tuesday **11**

Say it as you see it

Wednesday **12**

Use 'stress' as fuel for your advantage

Thursday **13**

Celebrate your accomplishments

Worm Moon

Friday **14**

Keep your thinking healthy

Saturday **15**

Compassion and kindness go a long away

Sunday **16**

Nurture your spirit

March

Monday 17   St Patrick's Day

*Wherever you go and whatever you do,
may the luck of the Irish be there with you*

Tuesday 18

The future starts here

Wednesday 19

Look for the win—win

Thursday 20

Life is a school and we are all here to learn

Worm Moon

Friday 21

Remember those who inspired you, and why

Saturday 22

Stay in a state of gratitude

Sunday 23

Stay on purpose and bring purpose to what you do

March

Most of us have trouble juggling. The woman who says she doesn't is someone whom I admire but have never met.

Barbara Walters

Monday **24**

Keep your finances in order

Tuesday **25**

Remember where you came from

Wednesday **26**

If you're going through hell, keep going

Thursday **27**

Stay connected with your parents

Friday **28**

It's all unfolding according to plan. Relax

New Moon
Clocks spring forward tonight

Saturday **29**

Share your sparkle wherever you are

Mother's Day

Sunday **30**

A mother's love is a blessing

March

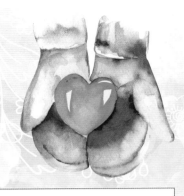

The most useful asset of a person is not a head full of knowledge but a heart full of love, with ears open to listen, and hands willing to help.

Rotku Wamura

Monday **31**

Take the time to get a medical check up

When your mother asks,
"Do you want a piece
of advice?"
It's a mere formality.
It doesn't matter if you
answer yes or no.
You're going to get it anyway.

Erma Bombeck

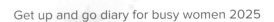

Bucket list for *April*

True beauty is not related to what colour your hair is or what colour your eyes are. True beauty is about who you are as a human being, your principles, your moral compass.

Ellen DeGeneres

April

Tuesday 01

Show up on time

Wednesday 02

Forget the mistakes of the past

Thursday 03

Anyone can hold the helm when the sea is calm

Friday 04

Don't worry about what you cannot control

Saturday 05

Go beyond the call of duty

Sunday 06

Your health is your wealth; guard it

Maybe the most important teaching is to lighten up and relax. It's such a huge help in working with our crazy mixed-up minds to remember that what we're doing is unlocking a softness that is in us and letting it spread. We're letting it blur the sharp corners of self-criticism and complaint.

Pema Chödrön

April

Monday **07**

Being happy is a way of being wise

Tuesday **08**

Create your home as a haven of peace and a piece of heaven

Wednesday **09**

Eating words rarely causes indigestion

Thursday **10**

You will see it when you believe it

Friday **11**

Let the past make you better, not bitter

Saturday **12**

No problem is insurmountable

Pink Moon

Sunday **13**

Take care of your body

April

We must believe that we are gifted for something, and that this thing, at whatever cost, must be attained.

Marie Curie

Monday **14**

Avoid buying what you do not need just because it's a bargain

---

Tuesday **15**

Today is that tomorrow you thought of yesterday

Wednesday **16**

Worrying is misuse of imagination

Thursday **17**

Creation is the spice of life

Good Friday
Friday **18**

Home is where the heart is

Saturday **19**

Keep two days a week worry free, Yesterday and Tomorrow

Easter Sunday
Sunday **20**

*Enjoy this day surrounded by friends,
family, and plenty of chocolate!*

April

I personally like being unique. I like being my own person with my own style and my own opinions and my own toothbrush.

Ellen DeGeneres

Monday **21**   Easter Monday

A busy mum is worth her weight in gold

Tuesday **22**

What about that new look you were promising yourself

Wednesday **23**

When is now a good time to do anything

Thursday 24

Don't be afraid to try something new

Friday 25

Self-acceptance is the doorway to greatness

Saturday 26

You are the source of your own experience

New Moon

Sunday 27

Trust your intuition

April

Let us always meet each other with a smile; for the smile is the beginning of love.

Mother Teresa

Monday **28**

Today is a good day to phone an old friend

Tuesday **29**

Allow extra time to get to where you're going

Wednesday **30**

When in doubt, take courage

Bucket list for *May*

> One is not born,
> but rather becomes,
> a woman.

Simone de Beauvoir

May

Life will break you. Nobody can protect you from that, and living alone won't either, for solitude will also break you with its yearning. You have to love. You have to feel. It is the reason you are here on earth. You are here to risk your heart. You are here to be swallowed up. And when it happens that you are broken, or betrayed, or left, or hurt, or death brushes near, let yourself sit by an apple tree and listen to the apples falling all around you in heaps, wasting their sweetness. Tell yourself you tasted as many as you could.

Louise Erdrich

Thursday **01**

Get enough sleep

Friday **02**

A family is usually a strong support network

Saturday **03**

Pay attention to your diet

Sunday **04**

Miracles do happen

May

The secret of getting ahead is getting started.

Sally Berger

Monday **05**
                       May Day Holiday

Be patient with children

Tuesday **06**

Make and keep promises

Wednesday **07**

Don't choose to suffer

Thursday **08**

Enjoy an ordinary day

Friday **09**

Some days are simply perfect

Saturday **10**

You are everything to someone

Mother's Day USA

Sunday **11**

Have a good laugh

May

To serve is beautiful, but only if it is done with joy and a whole heart.

Pearl S. Buck

Monday **12**   Flower Moon

Knock where the door is open

Tuesday **13**

Challenge yourself with a new goal

Wednesday **14**

Acknowledge the accomplishments of others

Thursday **15**

Don't jump to conclusions

Friday **16**

Be done with yesterday so it doesn't interfere with today

Saturday **17**

Have a beautiful, inspired day

Sunday **18**

Life is short; make fun of it

May

Our background and circumstances may have influenced who we are, but we are responsible for who we become.

Barbara Geraci

Monday **19**

Someone values your advice

Tuesday **20**

Respect yourself and others will respect you

Wednesday **21**

Change is inevitable, learn to embrace it

Thursday **22**

Be an attentive listener

Friday **23**

Visualise your desirable outcome

Saturday **24**

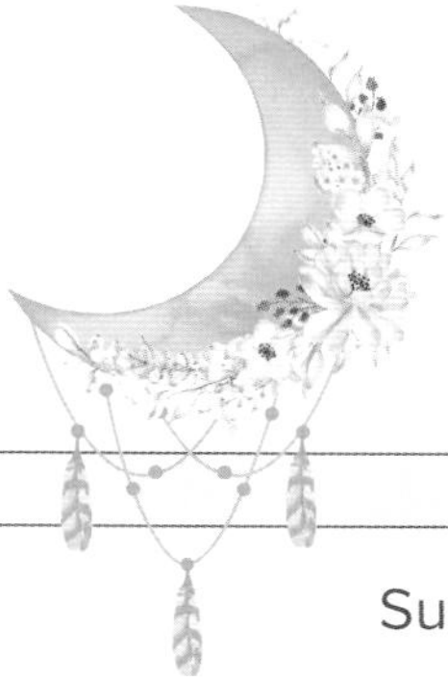

Put your dreams to work for you

Sunday **25**

Thoughts are seeds of deeds

May

You don't have to stay where you are; you can make a change.

Melissa Peterman

Monday **26**

Everyone has something unique worth saying

Tuesday **27**   New Moon

We build the ladder by which we rise

Wednesday **28**

Only complain to someone who can do something about it

Thursday **29**

Wherever you go, go with all your heart

Friday **30**

There is no 'no' in life

Saturday **31**

Take the time to get a medical check up

True happiness is not attained through self-gratification, but through fidelity to a worthy purpose.

Helen Keller

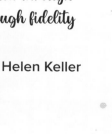

Caprese Salad with Salmon

INGREDIENTS:

- 1 bag of Mozzarella cheese (drain and dry off on kitchen paper)
- 1 Organic tomato
- Basil
  Green pesto
- Olive oil

METHOD:

Drain and dry the mozzarella on kitchen paper, then slice.

Slice the tomatoes.

Shred the basil without stalk.

Mix 1-2 teaspoons of pesto with 1 tablespoon of olive oil.

Arrange a layer of the cheese and tomatoes, top with shredded basil and drizzle the oil and pesto mixture on top. Contine layering in this manner finishing with olive oil and pesto.

Leave to marinate for 30 minutes. Eat on the day of preparation. It is best to season this dish at the table.

Delicious served with grilled salmon and cous cous.

Bucket list for *June*

Eat like you love yourself.
Move like you love yourself.
Speak like you love yourself.
Act like you love yourself.

Tara Stiles

June

The path to our destination is not always a straight one. We go down the wrong road, we get lost, we turn back. Maybe it doesn't matter which road we embark on. Maybe what matters is that we embark.

Barbara Hall

It takes great courage to faithfully follow what we know to be true.

Sara E. Anderson

Sunday **01**

Know the power of intention

June

The desire to reach for the stars is ambitious. The desire to reach hearts is wise

Maya Angelou - 1928-2014

Monday **02**   June Bank Holiday

Change thoughts of judgement to thoughts of compassion

Tuesday **03**

You are worthy of love

Wednesday **04**

Challenge your firmly held beliefs

Thursday 05

Your most valuable resource is your social support — reach out

Friday 06

There is time for everything — just not all at once

Saturday 07

Let go of doubt and fear

Sunday 08

Being an optimist is good for your health

June

The most effective way to do it, is to do it.
Amelia Earhart

Monday **09**

Everyone deserves to be understood

Tuesday **10**

Look. Listen. Choose. Act

Wednesday **11**   Strawberry Moon

Don't judge people by their relatives

Thursday 12

Time never flies faster than one day at a time

Friday 13

If you try, you might; if you don't, you won't

Saturday 14

Today is a good day to tidy your cupboards

Father's Day

Sunday 15

Nurture your relationships

June

If it doesn't feel right, don't do it.
That is the lesson, and that lesson
alone will save you a lot of grief.

Oprah Winfrey

Monday **16**

Respect your health and body

Tuesday **17**

Do what you know to do

Wednesday **18**

Relax, it's perfect the way it is

Thursday **19**

Stay focused on what you want

Friday **20**

Give up any pretence

Saturday **21**

You must do the thing you think you cannot do

Sunday **22**

Have a guilt free 'do-nothing' day

June

Creativity is a wild mind and a disciplined eye.

Dorothy Parker

Monday **23**

Keep calm and carry on

Tuesday **24**

Be an encourager not a critic

Wednesday **25**   New Moon

The only day that really matters is today

Thursday **26**

Be content within yourself

Friday **27**

Don't confuse opinions with facts

Saturday **28**

Give up the need to control

Sunday **29**

Use your support network

June

Stay focused on the positive as much as possible. Allowing yourself to be consumed by negativity will enhance nothing in your life.

Helen Reddy

Monday **30**
Be grateful for all that you have

Bucket list for *July*

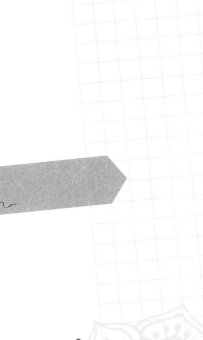

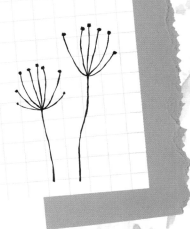

Look closely at the present you are constructing; it should look like the future you are dreaming.

Alice Walker

July

Often people attempt to live their lives backwards: they try to have more things, or more money, in order to do more of what they want so they will be happier.
The way it actually works is the reverse. You must first be who you really are, then, do what you need to do, in order to have what you want.

Margaret Young

Tuesday **01**

Fortune favours the brave

Wednesday **02**

Your intuition is always on your side

Thursday **03**

All you give is given to yourself

Friday **04**

Enjoy the outdoors

Saturday **05**

Self-expression is essential to life

Sunday **06**

Don't try and be a mind reader

July

When a woman becomes her own best friend life is easier.

Diane Von Furstenberg

Monday **07**

Visualise your best future

Tuesday **08**

Character is built daily

Wednesday **09**

It starts with you

Thunder Moon

Thursday **10**

Never send an email when you are upset

Friday **11**

Feel free to start something new

Orange Holiday NI

Saturday **12**

We all have our role to play

Sunday **13**

Listen to learn and understand

July

What would you do if you weren't afraid?

Sheryl Sandberg

Monday 14

Orange Holiday, Observed

Be clear on your ground rules

Tuesday 15

Plan a new adventure

Wednesday 16

Be the first to say 'sorry' when needed

Thursday 17

Conversation is an art, practice it

Friday 18

Widen your circle of friends

Saturday 19

Life is not just about getting by

Sunday 20

There are many precious moments beyond current obstacles

July

It is good to have an end to journey towards, but it is the journey that matters, in the end.

Ursula K LeGuin

Monday **21**

Beauty is in the eye of the beholder

Tuesday **22**

Have a good idea and nurture it

Wednesday **23**

Do it today, you may never be 'ready' enough

New Moon   Thursday **24**

It's your life, work to make it better

Friday **25**

Everything and everyone is connected

Saturday **26**

The truth is always transparent

Sunday **27**

Refuse to indulge in self-pity

July

Pleasure of love lasts but a moment.
Pain of love lasts a lifetime.

Bette Davis

Monday **28**

Everything can change in the blink of an eye

Tuesday **29**

Always keep a well-developed sense of humour

Wednesday **30**

Always do the sums, make sure they add up

Take the time to get a medical check up

We don't realize that, somewhere within us all, there does exist a supreme self who is eternally at peace.

Elizabeth Gilbert

If all the good people were clever
And all clever people were good
The world would be nicer than ever
We thought that it possibly could.
But somehow, 'tis seldom or never
The two hit it off as they should
The good are so harsh to the clever
The clever so rude to the good.

Dame Elizabeth Wordsworth
1840-1932

Bucket list for August

You have to have confidence in your ability, and then be tough enough to follow through.

Rosalynn Carter

August

Sometimes being a friend means mastering the art of timing. There is a time for silence. A time to let go and allow people to hurl themselves into their own destiny. And a time to prepare to pick up the pieces when it's all over.

Gloria Naylor

Remove those I want you to like me stickers from your forehead and, instead, place them where they truly will do the most good – on your mirror!

Susan Jeffers

Friday **01**

Treat yourself to a pampering day

Saturday **02**

Be clear and specific about what you want

Sunday **03**

Find your favourite place to sit and watch the world go by

August

Anyone can hide. Facing up to things, working through them, that's what makes you strong.

Sarah Dessen

Monday **04**   August Bank Holiday

In family life be completely present

Tuesday **05**

You are doing a great job

Wednesday **06**

Gratitude is happiness achieved

Thursday 07

Worrying will not change the outcome

Friday 08

Freedom brings responsibility

Sturgeon Moon

Saturday 09

Wisdom lies in what you have learned

Sunday 10

Consider travelling to somewhere you have never been

August

The question isn't who's going to let me; it's who is going to stop me.

Ayn Rand

Monday 11

You get stronger with every step

Tuesday 12

Become competent in your area of interest

Wednesday 13

It's ok to change your mind

Thursday **14**

Get to know yourself

Friday **15**

Effective communication is essential for happiness

Saturday **16**

Start your new healthy breakfast trend next week

Sunday **17**

Be your own unsinkable ship

August

Above all, be the heroine of your life, not the victim.

Nora Ephron

Monday **18**

Stay open and curious – it's all new

Tuesday **19**

Start your day with a definite purpose in mind

Wednesday **20**

Choose powerfully in the moment

Thursday 21

When your "WHY" is big enough you will find your "HOW"

Friday 22

Do not participate in gossip

New Moon

Saturday 23

Keep your cool

Sunday 24

Do something special for a dear friend

August

*Love is anterior to life, posterior to death,
initial of creation, and the exponent of earth.*

Emily Dickinson

Monday **25**

Get up, dress up and show up

Tuesday **26**

You cannot fail but you can fail to try

Wednesday **27**

Play the game of life ... just for the fun of it

Thursday **28**

Be willing to be open to something new

Friday **29**

See the beauty within yourself

Saturday **30**

Plan an "away-day" with your best friend

Sunday **31**

Stop doing what's not working for you

We wove a web in childhood.
A web of sunny air
We dug a spring in infancy.
Of water pure and fair
We sowed in youth a mustard seed.
We cut an almond rod.
We are now grown up to riper age.
Are they withered in the sod?

Charlotte Bronte

Bucket list for *September*

September

The pen that writes your life story must be held in your own hand.

Irene C. Kassorla

Monday **01**

Set yourself a 90-day challenge

Tuesday **02**

Self-acceptance is cheaper than cosmetic surgery

Wednesday **03**

Be a player not a spectator

Thursday **04**

To laugh at yourself is to love yourself

Friday **05**

You only fail when you refuse to get up and go again

Saturday **06**

There is never success without action

Sunday **07**

Harvest Moon

Challenge yourself to step outside your comfort zone

September

While we try to teach our children all about life, our children teach us what life is all about.

Angela Schwindt

Monday **08**

In conflict be fair and generous

Tuesday **09**

Smile when you answer the telephone

Wednesday **10**

Don't fear what you don't understand

Thursday **11**

Turn your problems into challenges

Friday **12**

Families are great training grounds

Saturday **13**

Set aside some quiet time

Sunday **14**

Let yourself be inspired

September

One of the most courageous decisions you will ever make is to finally let go of whatever is hurting your heart and soul.

Brigitte Nicole

Monday **15**

Avoid undue stress

Tuesday **16**

A good fence makes good neighbours

Wednesday **17**

Stay true to your values

Thursday 18

Abundance is everywhere

Friday 19

Be solution focused

Saturday 20

Go dancing

New Moon

Sunday 21

You really are worthy of love

September

Nothing is worth more than laughter. It is strength to laugh and to abandon oneself, to be light. Tragedy is the most ridiculous thing.

Frida Kahlo

Monday 22

Make the time to rekindle an old friendship

Tuesday 23

Your inner voice is not always your friend

Wednesday 24

Be daring / be different

Thursday **25**

Never be pushed into silence

Friday **26**

Share your concerns

Saturday **27**

Anger is one letter short of danger

Sunday **28**

Be flexible and flowing in the stream of life

September

I've learned over the years that when the mind is made up, this diminishes fear. Knowing what must be done does away with fear.

Rosa Parks

Monday **29**

Schedule a girls' night in

Tuesday **30**

Your inner voice is not always your friend

It's not what you do for your children, but what you have taught them to do for themselves, that will make them successful human beings.

Ann Landers

Bucket list for *October*

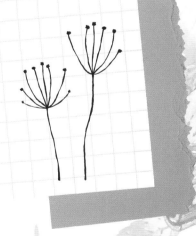

There is no chance, no destiny, no
fate that can circumvent or hinder
or control the firm resolve of a
determined soul.

Ella Wheeler Wilcox

October

Wednesday **01**

Change your thoughts and you change your world

Thursday **02**

Boundaries get blurred over time – keep redrawing the lines

Friday **03**

Look forward and ask why not

Saturday **04**

Daily exercise is conducive to wellbeing

Sunday **05**

Widen your social circle

October

No one's family is normal. Normalcy is a lie invented by advertising agencies to make the rest of us feel inferior.

Claire LaZebnik

Monday **06**

The written word is a crystallised thought

Tuesday **07**   Hunter's Moon

If in doubt, honour your word

Wednesday **08**

Do not get discouraged

Thursday 09

The truth is not always easy to hear, or speak

Friday 10

Well, done is better than well said

Saturday 11

Always try to see the 'big picture'

Sunday 12

Keep your house in order

October

The best career advice to give the young is, find out what you like doing best and get someone else to pay you for doing it.

Katherine Whilehaen

Monday **13**

A good book can be a good companion

Tuesday **14**

It's never the wrong time to do the right thing

Wednesday **15**

Remind yourself you are never alone

Thursday 16

It's what you do right now that matters

Friday 17

Where there's a will, there's a way

Saturday 18

We can all learn from children

Sunday 19

Be willing to forgive

October

Everybody knows if you are too careful you are so occupied in being careful that you are sure to stumble over something.

Gertrude Stein

Monday **20**

Do what you say you will do

Tuesday **21**   New Moon

You will be alright whatever happens

Wednesday **22**

For every effect there is a cause

Thursday **23**

Let go of negativity

Friday **24**

Do unto others as you would have others do unto you

Clocks fall back tonight   Saturday **25**

Decide what you want and the steps you need to get you there

Sunday **26**

Declutter; make space for new things in your life

October

Dignity and respect has to do with ... your personal power to make a difference by being true to the best within you and letting that truth shine through your words and actions. **Gail Pursell Elliott**

Monday 27   October Bank Holiday

Practice makes perfect

Tuesday 28   New Moon

Sometimes we need to go for a walk just to clear our head

Wednesday 29

Happy people carry their sunshine with them

Thursday **30**

Seek to understand before being understood

Halloween

Friday **31**

And ghouls just want to have fun

In truth a family is what you make it. It is made strong, not by number of heads counted at the dinner table, but by the rituals you help family members create, by the memories you share, by the commitment of time, caring, and love you show to one another, and by the hopes for the future you have as individuals and as a unit.

Marge Kennedy

Bucket list for *November*

To succeed, you have to do something and be very bad at it for a while. You have to look bad before you can look really good.

Barbara DeAngelis

November

I wanted a perfect ending. Now I've learned, the hard way, that some poems don't rhyme, and some stories don't have a clear beginning, middle, and end. Life is about not knowing, having to change, taking the moment, and making the best of it, without knowing what's going to happen next. Delicious ambiguity.

Gilda Radner

Saturday 01

Start a new winter hobby

Sunday 02

Differences enrich families

November

Woman must not accept; she must challenge. She must not be awed by that which has been built up around her; she must reverence that woman in her which struggles for expression.

Margaret Sanger

Monday **03**

It will go the way you say

Tuesday **04**   New Moon

There is a time for everything

Wednesday **05**   Beaver Moon (supermoon)

Don't be held back by a bad attitude

Thursday 06

Do today what you want to put off until tomorrow

Friday 07

If you mess up, fess up

Saturday 08

Smile at the person in the mirror often

Sunday 09

Move with the flow of life

November

Nothing will work unless you do.
Maya Angelou

Monday **10**

A trade not properly learnt is an enemy

Tuesday **11**

Take the initiative

Wednesday **12**

There is nothing to be gained by putting yourself down

Thursday **13**

Engage in lifelong learning

Friday **14**

If anger rises, think of the consequences

Saturday **15**

You are responsible for your own happiness

Sunday **16**

Listen to the advice of friends and loved ones

November

Let food be thy medicine and medicine be thy food.

Hippocrates

Monday **17**

You are a child of the universe

Tuesday **18**

You CAN deal with any situation

Wednesday **19**

Invite friends to dinner this weekend

New Moon   Thursday **20**

We each have the best of us at the heart of us

Friday **21**

Your speed doesn't matter, forward is forward

Saturday **22**

Listen to your body's messages

Sunday **23**

It's always great to remember people's names

November

A year from now you will wish you had started today.

Karen Lamb

Monday **24**

Smile regularly

Tuesday **25**

Work smart – time is money

Wednesday **26**

Have a conscious positive intention in every situation

Thursday **27**

Gratitude turns what we have into enough

Black Friday   Friday **28**

Having a sharp tongue can cut your own throat

Saturday **29**

Have a bath by candlelight, you deserve it

Sunday **30**

Take the time to get a medical check up

When you begin to touch your heart or let your heart be touched, you begin to discover that it's bottomless, that it doesn't have any resolution, that this heart is huge, vast, and limitless. You begin to discover how much warmth and gentleness is there, as well as how much space.

Pema Chodron

Bucket list for *December*

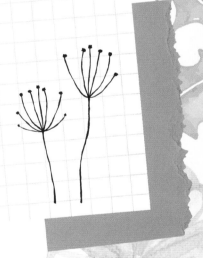

Trust yourself. Create the kind of self that you will be happy to live with all your life. Make the most of yourself by fanning the tiny, inner sparks of possibility into flames of achievement.

Golda Meir

December

Change your life today. Don't gamble on the future, act now, without delay.

Simone de Beauvoir

Monday **01**   Cyber Monday

Maybe a new look for Christmas?

Tuesday **02**

Everyone has a unique point of view

Wednesday **03**

Listen to your heart

Cold Moon (supermoon)   Thursday **04**

Good advice never gets old

Friday **05**

Act with integrity

Saturday **06**

It pays to hold your nerve

Sunday **07**

Take time out to listen to your favourite music

December

The thing that is really hard, and really amazing, is giving up on being perfect and beginning the work of becoming yourself.

Anna Quindlen

Monday 08

You can only do your best

Tuesday 09

With the new day comes new strength

Wednesday 10

A healthy outside starts on the inside

Thursday **11**

Focus on the greater good

Friday **12**

Remain warm and approachable

Saturday **13**

Make a list and check it twice

Sunday **14**

Remember the universe will unfold as it should

December

Adam and Eve had an ideal marriage. He didn't have to hear about all the men she could have married, and she didn't have to hear about the way his mother cooked.

Kimberly Broyles

Monday **15**

This life is not a dress rehearsal

Tuesday **16**

When principle is involved, don't budge

Wednesday **17**

Do what you love, the reward will follow

Thursday 18

Use your words intentionally – they have great power

Friday 19

Modern life guarantees distraction – stay focused

New Moon

Saturday 20

Your life is a hero's journey

Sunday 21

Feel the fear and do it anyway

December

May the world be kind to you, and may your own thoughts be gentle upon yourself.

Jonathan Lockwood Huie

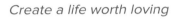

Monday **22**

Create a life worth loving

Tuesday **23**

Sort out your priorities

Wednesday **24**

Light a candle in memory of someone you loved and lost

Christmas Day

Thursday **25**

It's family and friends who really matter

St. Stephen's Day

Friday **26**

Be with the people who bring out the best in you

Saturday **27**

Where there is trust, no proof necessary

Sunday **28**

A helping hand is better than a load of advice

December

We are each gifted in a unique and important way. It is our privilege and our adventure to discover our own special light.

Mary Dunbar

Monday 29

If you don't need it, it is not a bargain

Tuesday 30

Have a clear vision for your future - visualise it to realise it

---

Wednesday 31   New Years Eve

Start the day with a hearty breakfast, tomorrow is a NEW YEAR

Christmas Trifle

INGREDIENTS:

- 100ml sherry
- 100g caster sugar
- 500g frozen fruit
- Few drops of vanilla essence
- 200g marble or plain madeira cake
- 300ml custard
- 300ml fresh cream
- Fresh raspberries or blueberries to decorate

METHOD:

Bring sherry, caster sugar & vanilla essence to boil, then reduce heat to form syrup.

Add frozen fruit, defrost in the liquid. (don't allow to lose shape)

Cool and pour over madeira cake.

Add custard

Cool overnight.

Add whipped cream.

Decorate with fresh raspberries or blueberries and serve.

THE FOUR AGREEMENTS

1. Be Impeccable With Your Word
Speak with integrity. Say only what you mean. Avoid using the word to speak against yourself or to gossip about others. Use the power of your word in the direction of truth and love.

2. Don't Take Anything Personally
Nothing others do is because of you. What others say and do is a projection of their own reality, their own dream. When you are immune to the opinions and actions of others, you won't be the victim of needless suffering.

3. Don't Make Assumptions
Find the courage to ask questions and to express what you really want. Communicate with others as clearly as you can to avoid misunderstandings, sadness and drama. With just this one agreement, you can completely transform your life.

4. Always Do Your Best
Your best is going to change from moment to moment; it will be different when you are healthy as opposed to sick. Under any circumstance, simply do your best, and you will avoid self-judgment, self-abuse and regret.

Miguel Ruiz

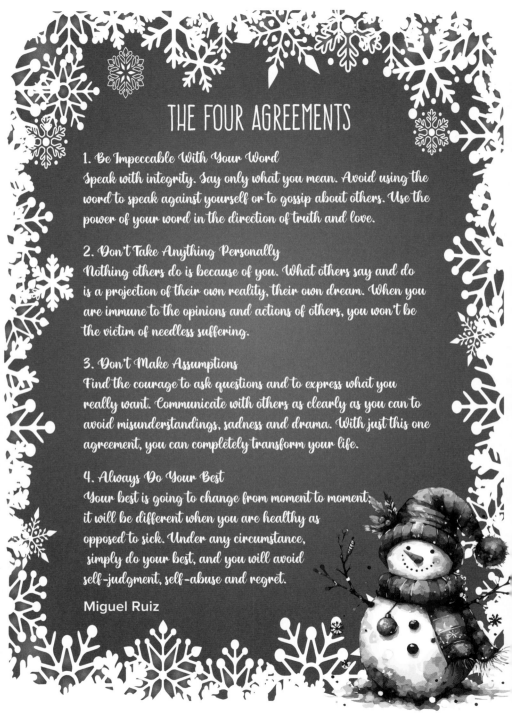

2026 CALENDAR

January

Su	Mo	Tu	We	Th	Fr	Sa
28	29	30	31	1	2	3
4	5	6	7	8	9	10
11	12	13	14	15	16	17
18	19	20	21	22	23	24
25	26	27	28	29	30	31

February

Su	Mo	Tu	We	Th	Fr	Sa
1	2	3	4	5	6	7
8	9	10	11	12	13	14
15	16	17	18	19	20	21
22	23	24	25	26	27	28

March

Su	Mo	Tu	We	Th	Fr	Sa
1	2	3	4	5	6	7
8	9	10	11	12	13	14
15	16	17	18	19	20	21
22	23	24	25	26	27	28
29	30	31	1	2	3	4

April

Su	Mo	Tu	We	Th	Fr	Sa
29	30	31	1	2	3	4
5	6	7	8	9	10	11
12	13	14	15	16	17	18
19	20	21	22	23	24	25
26	27	28	29	30	1	2

May

Su	Mo	Tu	We	Th	Fr	Sa
26	27	28	29	30	1	2
3	4	5	6	7	8	9
10	11	12	13	14	15	16
17	18	19	20	21	22	23
24	25	26	27	28	29	30
31	1	2	3	4	5	6

June

Su	Mo	Tu	We	Th	Fr	Sa
31	1	2	3	4	5	6
7	8	9	10	11	12	13
14	15	16	17	18	19	20
21	22	23	24	25	26	27
28	29	30	1	2	3	4

July

Su	Mo	Tu	We	Th	Fr	Sa
28	29	30	1	2	3	4
5	6	7	8	9	10	11
12	13	14	15	16	17	18
19	20	21	22	23	24	25
26	27	28	29	30	31	1

August

Su	Mo	Tu	We	Th	Fr	Sa
26	27	28	29	30	31	1
2	3	4	5	6	7	8
9	10	11	12	13	14	15
16	17	18	19	20	21	22
23	24	25	26	27	28	29
30	31	1	2	3	4	5

September

Su	Mo	Tu	We	Th	Fr	Sa
30	31	1	2	3	4	5
6	7	8	9	10	11	12
13	14	15	16	17	18	19
20	21	22	23	24	25	26
27	28	29	30	1	2	3

October

Su	Mo	Tu	We	Th	Fr	Sa
27	28	29	30	1	2	3
4	5	6	7	8	9	10
11	12	13	14	15	16	17
18	19	20	21	22	23	24
25	26	27	28	29	30	31

November

Su	Mo	Tu	We	Th	Fr	Sa
1	2	3	4	5	6	7
8	9	10	11	12	13	14
15	16	17	18	19	20	21
22	23	24	25	26	27	28
29	30	1	2	3	4	5

December

Su	Mo	Tu	We	Th	Fr	Sa
29	30	1	2	3	4	5
6	7	8	9	10	11	12
13	14	15	16	17	18	19
20	21	22	23	24	25	26
27	28	29	30	31	1	2

NOTES

NOTES

TO SEE OUR FULL RANGE OF DIARIES AND JOURNALS, PLEASE VISIT OUR WEBSITE:

www.getupandgodiary.com

**GetUpandGo
Publications**
WE ASPIRE TO INSPIRE

CONTACT US

Post: Get Up and Go Publications Ltd,
Unit 7A Cornhill Business Park, Ballyshannon,
Co Donegal, Ireland F94 C4AA

Email: info@getupandgodiary.com
Tel: 071 98 45938 or 085 1764297 (office hours)

ORDER FORM

The Irish Get Up and Go Diary (paperback), €12.95/£11   Quantity ☐

The Irish Get Up and Go Diary (padded cover), €18.50/£16   Quantity ☐

The Get Up and Go Diary (paperback), €12.95/£11   Quantity ☐

Get Up and Go Diary for Busy Women (paperback), €12.95/£11   Quantity ☐

Get Up and Go Diary for Busy Women (padded cover), €18.50/£16   Quantity ☐

Get up and Go Young Person's Diary €12.95/£11   Quantity ☐

Daily Guide to Good Health and Wellbeing (paperback), €16.50/£14   Quantity ☐

Get Up and Go Gratitude Journal (padded cover), €18.50/£16   Quantity ☐

Get Up and Go Wallplanner (size: A1), €4/£4   Quantity ☐

Total number of copies ☐

ADD POSTAGE

Standard postage for 1 copy:

Ireland: €3.45   Great Britain: €5.50   Europe: €5.50   USA: €8.50   Aus/NZ: €9.50

For tracking charges and bulk postage please refer to our website or call 071 98 45938

I enclose cheque/postal order for (total amount including P+P):_____

Name: _____

Address: _____

Phone no: _____

Email:_____

For general enquiries or to pay by credit/debit card, please contact us 071 98 45938 or 085 1764297 during office hours